Gardening for Children

and their

Grandparents

by

Barbara Hyde Boardman

Character illustrations by Scott Johnson
All other illustrations and page layout by Daina Penn
Cover design by Barbara Hyde Boardman

Hyde Boardman, Barbara
    Gardening for Children and Their Grandparents
    ISBN 978-0-692-40094-4 $20.00

Printed in the United States of America by
Brent Engelhardt
Henry Wurst, Incorporated
Western Region
5000 Osage Street, Suite 100
Denver, CO 80221

Table of Contents

Preface

This book is intended to bridge the gap between grandparent and grandchild. It gives the grandparent an opportunity to introduce the joy of gardening to a child without making it seem like a chore.

It also can be an introduction for the new immigrant to the pathway to becoming a citizen. By knowing and understanding the reasons for the various holidays we celebrate, they may come closer to integrating into their new country without abandoning the customs of their former land.

The book may also be the how-to for all those who have been urged to dig up a plot in the school grounds, the city park, or an abandoned space to grow their own food, to lessen the carbon footprint, or to give an excuse for their own existence.

Author has seen this national phenomena three times. The first was observed during WWII when we all were urged to have a "victory garden"; the second was during the Hippie Era of 1960-1980 when hippies endured living in the abandoned mine shafts of Colorado to tend their gardens beside mountain streams. Now the third time around, we see the First Lady digging up a portion of the White House lawn to plant a vegetable garden that will be emulated throughout the land. Too often these gardens have been observed to be growing infested with weeds, with no thought or knowledge of irrigation, fertilization or countless other horticultural procedures. By giving the reader a step-by-step direction in the successful growing of vegetables this book may be a small step in relieving hunger, but a large step in introducing gardening as a reliever of stress, as a pleasant exercise, and an introduction into the camaraderie of gardeners everywhere.

If this book could urge the immigrant to become an American or a lifelong resident to become a better American, or grandparents and grandchildren to have a closer relationship, would the world be a better place?

Chapter 1

Arrival

On a bright sunny day in Littleton, Colorado, a pair of grandparents waited anxiously for the arrival of three of their many grandchildren whom they had agreed to care for during the next nine months while the parents have gone on a mission.

Grandfather: "What shall we talk about with them? Are we supposed to play games with them? I don't remember how to play children's games.

Grandmother: Oh, no. They won't want to play games with us—they will be working on their devices and not interested in us. I'm just worried about what to feed them. Ann just said that "they will eat anything". I'm not so sure about that.

Grandfather: You know, I've been thinking about what they should call us. Grandsomething_____: is a very long word for them to use when they talk to us. Why don't we tell them to call us GF for me, and GM for you?

Grandmother: I think that's a great idea. Hello, GF! Both laughing. Well, here they come!

Liam: Where are the Rocky Mountains?

Melinda: I'm 'Dopted!

Declan: Is there chickens and fish where you live?

GF: Lots of questions, and all will be answered. Let's introduce ourselves first. I'm your grandfather and this is your grandmother. We have decided that you should call us GF and GM—the first initial of grandfather and grandmother. Is that Okay with you?

Liam: I'm Liam and I'll be happy to call you GF and GM.

Melinda: I'm Melinda and I'm the youngest of us kids.

Declan: I'm Declan and I'm so glad to be here, GF and GM.

3

Chapter 2
A Sly Introduction to Gardening

Late that night.

GF: Well, they ate a pretty good supper. I guess we'll be eating a lot of hamburgers for the next six months.

GM: I'll try to insert a few vegetables now and then.

GF: Well, that brings up a thought I've had. Do you suppose we could get them to go outside and learn how to grow the vegetables? The garden needs spading since I didn't get around to it last fall. We could begin by showing them a shovel and how to use it.

GM: It won't hurt to try. I'm sure they were instructed to mind us without fail.

Next morning.

GF: Okay, kids, before we go outside, you must put on your gloves. Your grandmother and I have a pair for each of you. Let's see if they fit.

All Three: My gloves feel great. Never had gloves before.

GF: Well, they fit well enough, let's go outside this evening and I'll show you a new way to use your muscles!

Melinda: I don't have any muscles.

GF: Well, maybe we can find some for you. Boy's, help me carry these four shovels to the garden!

Chapter 3

Learning How to Spade with a Shovel

GF: Here you are, Liam and Declan. These are called shovels. In the East they are called "spades", but this is the West and we call them 'shovels'. For you, Melinda, here is your grandmother's shovel. Your Dad calls it "Mother's Teaspoon", but it's just your size for spading the garden.

Liam: He picks up a small amount of soil. "Is this the way? What am I supposed to do with this stuff?"

GF: Let's put the soil down and I'll show you how to use the shovel first. We'll start right at the border of the garden here. Grab your shovel and point it straight down into the soil and then push it all the way into the soil like this. Then pull back on the top of the handle and lift the shovel full of soil and turn it over and dump it back to where it came from. See me!

Liam: Whew, that's heavy work. You want me to do another one?

GF: I'll do one next to yours, then you, Declan and Melinda, do one next to mine!

Declan: Don't you want us to smooth out the dirt?

GF: No, we want to leave the soil rough and humpy so that the snow and frost will go down deep and kill the eggs of the bad bugs. It's only March and the soil is still cold. And, by the way we don't call it dirt, we call it SOIL. Dirt is something nasty. Soil is where we grow the food that we eat.

All three: Okay, we'll call it 'soil'.

GM: Won't you all want to tell your parents about how you spaded the garden when we skype this week?

All: Yes, and can we show them a picture? Grandmother takes a snapshot with her camera.

GM: Now we can hold it up to the screen to show your parents.

GARDEN FULLY SPADED

Chapter 4
Choosing the Seeds

GF and GM alternately: Now that your lesson time is over, we have time to choose the vegetable seeds that we are going to grow. Here is a catalog of pictures for you (passing out catalogs), and we'll begin with the first pages which are in alphabetical order, and it begins with "Artichokes" which we can't grow here because our winters are too cold; so we go to the next one, which is "BEANS".

We like to grow pole beans: this means the ones that climb up a pole rather than make a bush near the ground. Which ones do you think you would like for us to grow, Liam.

Beans

Liam: I like beans sometimes, so I think the big picture of beans looks the best.

GM: That would be "Tenderpod" which means they are not hard to bite into. Okay? We turn to the next page and we see BEETS!

Melinda: I don't like Beets. Let's not grow THEM!

Beets

GM: Oh, yes we have to grow them every year. I'll pickle some and I know you will like them.

Melinda: um-m.

GF: Next we find the pages for Broccoli, Brussel's sprouts, and cabbage. We only need two plants of broccoli, two cabbages and five of the sprouts, and we grow them in the same row, because it's cheaper to buy those plants than to buy the seeds and grow them from seed. We'll skip to the carrot section.

Broccoli   Brussel's sprouts

Cabbage   Carrots

Declan laughing: I like carrots. I can pronounce "Sweet Treat Hybrid". So let's grow those!

GF: Good choice, Declan. A plant with the word "hybrid" in its name means it will be extra strong and extra tasty. If you will look further, it says "good top attachment", which means that the leaves and stems will be extra strong and not snap off when you pull on them at harvest time.

GM: Next is Cauliflower, which is another veggie that we don't have room for a whole row; so we buy one or two plants at the garden center at planting time.

Cauliflower

All three: We don't even know what colly-flower tastes like.

GM: You will like it when I fix it with cream sauce and cheese.

GF: Next is Celery. We eat a lot of celery. Two rows of it, one on either side of the drip hose.

Melinda: I'll mark it down. Next is Corn.

GF: We don't have room for corn. It takes growing three rows to get it to pollinate right; so we let the good growers in the little town of Olathe grow our corn and we buy lots of it to keep them in business. We may have time for a field trip to see a corn field at Olathe.

Corn

Melinda: Next is Cucumber. Do we grow that one?

GF: Yes, but we only need one vine to train up the trellis at the edge of the garden, so we will also buy that plant.

Cucumber

GM: The next is Eggplant. Since I'm the only one who likes "eggplant" I will buy one and I'll fix it in the oven and see if you like it.

Eggplant

Melinda: Good deal, GM. Next is g-a-r-l-i-c. Jarlic?

Liam: No, little one. It's "Garlic" and we don't like it!

Garlic

GF: We can skip that one then. And next is Kale. *GM makes a note in her head to plant a few garlic in the onion plot. She uses it in seasoning stews and roasts.*

Kale

GM: Kale is very "fashionable" now—supposed to be loaded with vitamins. I don't think we've ever grown it. How about it, GF?

GF: Well, let's try a row and we can always pull it up if we don't like it and plant something else.

Melinda: Lettuce is one we all like. Shall we grow a double row?

Lettuce

GF: Absolutely. We like "Buttercrunch" which makes little heads you can pick one at a time for a whole salad for each one. Then we grow an old time one called "Black Seeded Simpson". I don't know who Mr. Simpson was but he selected a fine variety.

Melinda: Next looks like a picture of Cantaloupe. Oh, I see, it's M for melon. That is for all the melons.

Melon

GF: Yay! You're a pretty smart kid for eight years old! (Melinda stands a little straighter). This is another vegetable we grow only one of, and it's always Burpee's Ambrosia Hybrid. Way back in the forties, Burpee developed a hybrid of what turned out to be the very best cantaloupe of all —"Ambrosia", so we will squander $3.95 for a packet of seed and only plant one of them in GM's flower bed.

GM: Next is Okra, and we don't grow this one because our summers are not hot enough. We think they are hot, but those who live in the South say that the temperature must be over 100° to grow good Okra. I'm not sure how to cook it anyway. I'd have to get out the BIG cookbook.

Okra

11

GF: Onions are next—one of our favorites. We always share an order of sets with our neighbor because one order is more than we have room for, that way, we get all three types: yellow sweet Spanish, Cippolini Red, and Texas Supersweet (white). Then we plant a little row of scallions too. We save a big area for onions. Mark off three rows.

Onion

Declan: Next is Peas. We all like them. Should we grow two rows?

GF: Yes, indeed. Let's grow Sugar Snap in a two -row method I will show you, and we will grow a row of marigolds right next to the peas so that the bees will be attracted to them and to the pea blossoms for pollination.

Peas

GM: We're getting toward the last. Next is Pepper, and it's another that we don't use much of; so we buy four or five plants to plant in between the tomatoes.

Peppers

GF: Well, we have come to Potato and we have a special place where we grow our potatoes each year —it's next to the neighbor's fence and will be next to the pole beans. We will have one hill of sweet potatoes and two hills of white potatoes.

We grow the big "Yukon Gold" potato as well as one little hill of " Irish Cobbler" as a tip of the hat to your Irish ancestors.

The sweet potato we favor is "Georgia Jet". Each plant will give 5-10 pounds, which is enough for us and for the neighbor's.

Potato

Liam: Now we're down to one we will like the best, just not to eat. It's the PUMPKIN! Can we grow a big one, GF, and carve it for Halloween?

Pumpkin

GF: We can try. I'll have to go to the Library to look at the book they have on growing big pumpkins. We'll grow in the other flower bed and hope it doesn't smother the flowers.

Declan: Next is Radish! I like these if they don't get too hot.

Radish

GM: We grow Cherry Belle in the same row as the carrots. They take only about three weeks before they are ready to pull to eat, and the carrots are slow to germinate. The radishes mark the row of carrots so we don't step on them.

GF: S is for Spinach and we grow just one row. It is for very early spring, like now, and can all be harvested quickly; then we will plant it again in the early fall. Bloomsdale Long Standing is the variety we like.

Spinach

Melinda: Squash is next. Is anybody else getting tired?

ALL: yes, Let's quit!

GF and GM: Not so fast! But we have only three more to go: Squash, Turnips, and Tomatoes. We'll make it easy for you. We don't grow squash of any kind, because the farmers here can grow it better than we can. The supermarkets will have all of the squash: Zucchini, Summer Squash and the big winter squashs: Butternut, Spaghetti, and Acorn.

Liam: Then that leaves only Tomatoes and Turnips.

GF: Every year we think we ought to try the new kinds of tomato, but the two kinds of tomato that we always grow are Better

Tomato

Boy and Celebrity: then we grow one of the little plum tomato San Marzano—so that we can make your Nana's special salsa.

Declan: That brings us to Turnips.

GF: This is one that we don't plant until after the Summer Solstice.

Turnip

Children: Whatzat?

GF: That is the 21st of June, the longest day of the year. Each one has a different question: Will it show in the sky? Will the sun be the same size? Does the sun turn a different color?

GF: Yes and no to those questions. We will show it to you on the 21st of June! What does it do to the turnips on that day? Nothing. It is just a date that is late for planting, but best for turnips because they will be sweet and crisp in late fall. Mark off a double row for turnips, but put it's marker up.

GF: We're down to W of the alphabet, which means WATERMELON. GM and I have talked it over and decided to plant one watermelon plant in her flower garden so that you kids can see how they grow and what a home-grown watermelon tastes like.

Liam: Will it be in GM's flower garden because it will grow best there?

Watermelon

GF: No, it's because that's the only place there is room for it to roam around and get the best sunlight.

14

GM: Now it is late and it's off to bed for all of you

GF: Ha, no complaint there—they all trotted off like a flock of sheep.

Will Henry (GF): I think the first two days have gone really well.

Ellen (GM): Yes, but now I have the home-schooling to deal with. Ann has sent me all the materials and I can see how it is done day-to-day, but it seems a lot different than when I was teaching fourth grade.

Will Henry: You will be fine. I'm sure they know the routine and I've fixed up the guest room with the desks we bought. I think the lighting is okay. Is there anything else I can do to help?

Ellen: No, you've been a dear. I've just got the jitters.

Will Henry: Come over to my shoulder.

Chapter 5

Shopping for Seeds

GF: Today after lessons, we are going shopping for the seeds we picked out yesterday. Remember that we chose the seeds from the catalog. Our local garden center carries the same brand of seeds; so we can patronize a local garden center and still get the quality seeds. Everyone into the van!

GM: Here is a clipboard for each of you. You decide which part of the alphabet you want, and you will see the list on the first page of your list. There is a pencil attached; so please, please mark off the ones you have chosen. Off you go.

Liam, Declan, and Melinda arrive at the garden center: Wow! Wow! Wow! Look at this place. Look at all the colors, Look at all the flowers. Where are the Seeds? Where is a basket to put them in? Liam passes out the baskets.

Declan: Well, here are the seeds. Now let's try to find the kind of each one that we picked. The seeds are in alphabetical order here in the rack——see?

Liam: Okay, GF, we've finished picking all the ones that we wanted, but there were some that the rack did not have.

GF: That means we will have to order from the catalog back home. So let's show you how to pay for the ones you have here. Step up to the counter with your baskets, please. Now show the clerk your baskets and she will enter them in her machine, See? Now, this is my credit card.

All Three: Oh, yes, we know what a credit card is. Mom and Dad use it all the time to pay for EVERYTHING!

GF: (Aside: "Well, let's hope they paid the bill at the end of the month too). Okay, Give the clerk the card and see how she shoves it through? That means the total amount of the seeds goes on the bill that comes to our house at the end of the month.

They arrive back at home.

GF: Okay, now back into the house to order the seeds that the garden center did not have.

Liam: Can you find the ones the store did not have?

Melinda: Oh, sure I have them right here.

GF: You see the seed catalog phone number right here? Call it and when someone answers, you say, "May I place an order, please?" Then they will answer yes and you begin

giving them each number of the plant you want. See those numbers in black print beside each picture? That's the number they want. When you have finished, give her the number of the credit card, and the name (mine) and they will give you an approximate date of when the seeds will arrive, and that's all there is to it.

Liam: Wow! Using a credit card makes me a real grown-up!

GF: Well, Not quite, but you're gettin' there! Now off you go to slide on the slope or whatever you want to do.

Later that night: The grandparents are discussing the day.

Ellen: "It's hard to believe that they are adapting so fast to us, to our home and using the garden tools."

Will Henry: "I think they were instructed by their parents, and also because they are used to moving to different countries often, seeing new things.

Ellen: "Yes, I'm sure. Let's hope we can continue to interest them."

Chapter 6
Soil Preparation, Drip Irrigation

GF: Today is the day you get to pick up your tools and become real gardeners, kids! We may even have time to plant a few seeds. Remember! Sunscreen. Then gloves.

All three: Yay! I want the one I had when we first came.

GF: We used the shovels when you first came to spade the soil, remember, now we're going to smooth it out with the Bow Rake. Watch me. I first turn this rake over so that I use the bow side to move it back and forth across the soil to smooth out the humps that we left last week.

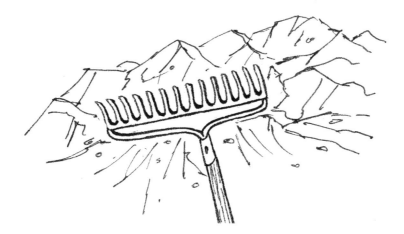

Declan: Wow, this is really easy, and the soil looks so nice when it's finished.

GF: Each of you take a turn and we'll soon be done.

Next, we are going to walk or run around on the soil a little to settle the air out of it and make it ready for the drip system.

Declan: Running around is what we do! Run, run, run!

GF: Okay, that's enough. Now this is the drip system. I'm going to lay it out on the soil in a way so that each hose will water a double row of vegetables.

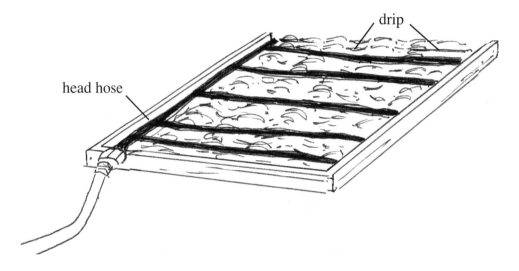

GF: This is where I fasten the beginning of the hose to the hose that goes to the water faucet. Can you help me screw it onto the water faucet?

That's right. Now let's turn it on a little to see if there are any leaks. The big hose is the head hose. All the drip hoses that go down each row are attached to the head hose. I don't see any leaks; so that means I don't have to fix leaks this year!

Now we lay out a regular hose along the fence where we will grow the pole beans and the potatoes and the cole crops. Both this hose and the head hose of the drip hoses are attached to the faucet which is attached to a little computer in the garage that I can set the water to run on the day and time the garden needs water.

Footnote: www.dripworks.com, leevalley.com

Liam: And that must save you going back and forth to change the hoses, doesn't it?

GF: It does for sure. Now before we quit for the day, we're going to choose the "Pea Sticks" and mark the rows. Come over this way to see the little pile of brush I saved after the spring pruning was finished. Pick out pieces that have lots of stems, like this one. I placed big sticks at the end of each row and I've attached a wire between them.
Now we tie the brush to the wire so that the peas will climb and attach to the wires. This procedure takes only a few minutes.

GF: Melinda, you are going to be our "marker". Here is a handful of markers and a list of what we chose to grow.

Melinda: Yay! I get to do something!

GF: Boys, you will be making the rows.; She will call out the name of the vegetable, and you will make a row for it. I'll be the one telling you how far apart and any other directions. This is a Warren hoe. I don't know who Warren was but he sure did invent a hoe with a curious ability that no other hoe has.

GM: All of the tools we use go way back in time, all the way to when the first human got smart and learned how to plant a seed, and then picked up a stick to dig the hole to plant the seed, then fashioned the stick to have a pointy end and an edge, and that became the first tool. Wait to see what else the Warren hoe can do when we plant the seeds tomorrow.

Next Day.

Liam: Okay, I'm ready to use the Warren hoe. What do I do first?

GF: Use the tip of the pointy end to draw the row into the soil next to the drip line to make a little furrow like this. Call out the name, Melinda.

Melinda: It would be TOMATO, and I have three markers ready to put down.

GF: So here they are, Liam. We are going to have two big tomatoes and one little San Marzano. We'll make them equidistant like this. Go ahead and place them, then we have room beside our tomatoes to grow peppers between them. Can you skip through the markers, Melinda, to find the pepper markers?

Melinda: Yes, here they are (as she hands them to GF).

Declan: And now we're ready for the next row. What is it, Melinda?

Melinda: It's lettuce.

GF: We' re going to grow two rows of it, one on each side of the drip hose; so make two rows on either side, Declan. One will be for Buttercrunch, and one for Black Simpson.

GF: The next row is for carrots, and, remember, we were going to grow radishes in the same row because the radishes will come up and grow to eating size before the carrot seeds even knew the radishes were there. So two rows once again, Declan.

Melinda: Next come beets— two rows once again.

Declan: Done.

Melinda: Next is Peas.

Liam: Pea sticks sort of placed and marked! Liam ties each pea stick to the wire that is stretched between a stake at the ends of the row.

Melinda: Next is Peppers, and we saved room for them between the tomatoes.

GF: That's right, Melinda. Remember this is a warm season crop so we wait until the weather is warmer to plant the peppers.

Liam: Marker saved for Peppers!

Melinda: Next is Celery.

Declan: Two rows marked and made.

Melinda: Next is Spinach.

Liam: Two rows made for spinach.

Melinda: Next is Herbs.

GM: Those rows are reserved for the cilantro and basil I need for salsa, as well as for a few seeds of marigolds planted with the herbs for the bees to find. As each bee visits a marigold, it will go on to visit the bean and the pea blooms, thus giving us more green beans and peas to eat.

Declan: Little lecture on pollination noted and two rows marked and made. Laughter follows before they all concentrate on making and marking the rows.

Melinda: One long row along the neighbor's fence for the pole beans.

Liam: One long row marked along the neighbor's fence.

Melinda: One short row for potatoes up next to the pole beans, also next to the neighbor's fence.

Liam: One short row made and marked.

Melinda: One short row along the neighbor's fence for Brussel's sprouts, cauliflower, cabbage, and broccoli.

Liam: Another short row for sprouts, cauliflower, cabbage, broccoli.

GF: That's all for today, kiddos! We'll plant them all, or most of them tomorrow.

Children: Let's get our skate boards!

Chapter 7

Planting at Last

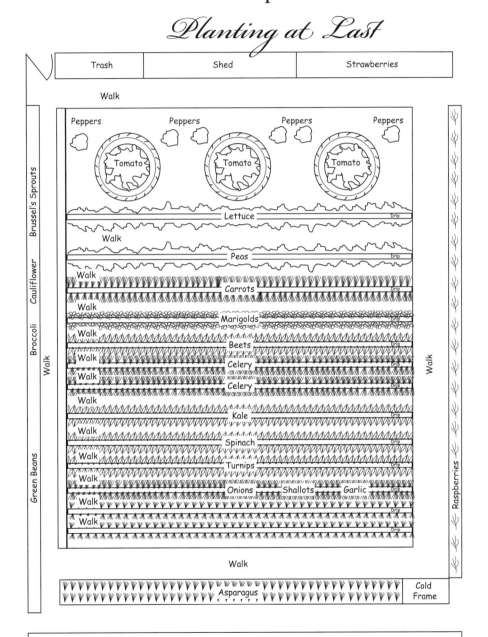

Trash	Shed	Strawberries

Walk

Peppers   Peppers   Peppers   Peppers

Tomato   Tomato   Tomato

Lettuce — Drip

Walk

Peas — Drip

Walk
Carrots — Drip
Walk
Marigolds — Drip
Walk
Beets — Drip
Walk
Celery — Drip
Walk
Celery — Drip
Walk
Kale — Drip
Walk
Spinach — Drip
Walk
Turnips — Drip
Walk
Onions — Shallots — Garlic — Drip
Walk — Drip
Walk — Drip

Walk

Asparagus   Cold Frame

House

25

GF (singing): It's a bright, sunny day in the 'marnin!!

Liam (singing): It's a bright sunny day today!

GM: I have almost all the seeds, except for the ones that have not arrived in the mail as yet, in order of their rows. No gloves needed today, guys, but we do need sunscreen and sunglasses. Planting is a very delicate business.

GF: We will need the Warren hoe again, and I will show you a new thing it can do. Let's go out into the garden. The first things we have to do is to set up the bean strings. See them, here? There are u-shaped prongs that are pushed into the ground. We will attach the strings for the beans to climb on at planting time. We don't plant beans until the soil is warm and it is too early now. We wet down each of the rest of the rows. Declan, why don't you take the hose, turn it on just a little bit? Do you think you can hold the hose over each row to wet the soil in the bottom of each row?

Declan: I can try but I'm going to get my feet muddy.

GM: That's all right. We'll clean them up when we finish and put the papers down on the paths. It's okay to step in the paths now. We want the soil in the rows to be wet so that each seed has moisture to begin germinating.

Melinda: I have all the seeds in order to plant each one.

GF: Good, Melinda. We'll start with the lettuce. It has a peculiar need. It needs a little light to germinate.

Liam: Oh, new word, new word, and I already know what it means. It means to come up! To come to life!

GF: Well, that's a good definition. What is happening is that the seed swells with the water we're going to give it, and with the lettuce, we just give it a little covering so that it will get a little sun, and the leaves will unfold from inside the seed and stretch upward to the sunlight. That's germination, and it will happen in just a few days.

GM: Here is the seeder and I have put a few seeds in it, Liam, and now you need to straddle the lettuce row; so put a foot on each side, but be careful not to step on the drip hose. Now use the Seeder by pressing on the button to make one seed come out. Hold it over the row. Did you see the seed come out?

Liam: Yes, I saw it.

Melinda: Yes, yes. I saw it too!

GM: Now I'm putting down the little piece of cardboard that is four inches square. It will tell you where to put the next seed.

Melinda: Okay, I planted the next seed and I put down the cardboard again.

GM: You're off and running. Now you probably don't need to put the cardboard down each time you plant a seed. You can estimate with your eyes the four inches, can't you?

Melinda: Yes, I think so, so here I go with the Buttercrunch. *(Twenty seconds later)* And now I'm at the end; so I need the Black Simpson. This is easy.

GM: I'm so glad you are closer to the ground so that it's easy. It's not easy for your grandfather and I.

Melinda: I'm done, now, GF, show us how to cover them.

GF: Everybody gather around. Give me the Warren hoe. I will stand as you did, Declan, and I turn over the hoe so that the two-prong side is downward, see? Now I place it over the row with the seeds and pull it slowly. See, it pulls just a little soil over the top of the seeds. It's a very smart hoe. Okay both rows of lettuce are now planted. Now we use our feet to push down gently on the soil to snug it over the seeds and push them into the soil. Now's whose next to try it?

Liam: I'm the oldest, so I should be last to do it. Go on, Melinda.

All three children take a turn and gleefully plant each row until all except one are planted.

GF: We leave one row for the turnips. We will plant them later, as well as the long row next to the fence for the green beans and a space for the potatoes, sweet potatoes, broccoli and Brussel's sprouts.

GF: There's still daylight. A farmer never goes in to supper until the sun is low on the horizon. Tell me, all of you. Is the sun going down?

All: It is, it is!

GM: Well, supper is NOT waiting because the farmer's wife has been out here playing with you. You kids go out front and play while I go in and do the cooking and call you in to dinner.

Chapter 8

Waiting, Waiting

GF: While we are waiting for the seeds to germinate there is one more task you kids might like to do—mow the lawn very slowly.

Liam: Yay! I'm biggest, I get to push!

GF: You all get a turn. It's in the garage, Let's go.

At the garage GF pulls out the mower, removes the cover, sets the blades to mow very short, and begins pulling the cord to get it started. After a few pulls the motor turns over and runs smoothly.

GF: Now see this lever? I'm going to push it down just a little and then push "forward" and it begins to move slowly. "So you, Liam, get to put your hands on the handle first.

Each one takes a turn at using the self-propelled lawn mower.

GF: Now we're going to dump the catcher bag full of the clippings into a bag to be saved. We will use these clippings to mulch. That's a new word for you that we will learn how to do in a few weeks.

Five days have passed.

The children have anxiously inspected the planted rows with anticipation each day. On the fifth day, Liam thinks he sees a tiny green sprout in the lettuce row.

Liam: Hurrah, Hurrah! I see the first sprout! It's so small, you can barely see it.

GM: It will grow a little each day.

The others gather around and confirm that they also see the first sprout.

GF: Seeing the first sign of germination means that we need to check the amount of moisture in the soil. Stick your fingers into the soil gently. Do you feel some wetness?

They all agree that they feel some wet soil.

GF: It's a very critical time for a seed. Too much water would drown the cells that are just expanding. Not enough water would cause the cells to dry up and die. What we need to do now is have patience and check each day until these little sprouts have the strength to begin growing. So go out and slide the slope with your boards, and we will check the garden again tomorrow.

GM: As the children disappear. I'm so glad we live where kids can play safely out in the street. The slope is just perfect for skate-boards. Who would have thought of that when all of us built our homes in this little subdivision?

GF: The skate boards are the darndest thing I've ever seen. We certainly would never have had them when I was a kid. If I tried to ride one now I'm sure I would break my neck.

Chapter 9
Beans, Onions, Potatoes & Herbs

GF: Today is May 10th. This is the day of the average last frost. Average means that all the last-frost dates were added up and May 10 turned out to be the most average date. We'll take a chance and go out to plant something. I have a bag of onion sets that we can plant. You will also need to put on your gloves.

Declan: What's a "set"?

GF: It's just a term to mean "a few" or "a bunch".

Melinda: They look just like little onions.

GF: That's right. They are little onions that will grow into big onions during the summer. Everyone take one.

They each take one and GF says as he pushes it into the soil. "We push it into the soil up to the second knuckle of the index finger."

Chorus: Which is my index finger and where is my "cuckle"?

GF shows each one the knuckle of the index finger. " The knuckle of your index fingers is not deep enough, so use your third joint to measure how deep to push the onion set."

They all try this maneuver while GF marks the rows for the onions with the hoe.

GF: We still have the potatoes and the green beans, sprouts, broccoli, and cabbage to plant. Let's go over to their place and get started. We plant each green bean seed with the little dark spot on the seed facing down. Each one takes a seed to find the dark spot.

Melinda: What's so special about the dark spot. Is this the spot where the root comes out of the seed?

GF: That's a hard question and I don't know the answer. It's just how bean seeds have been planted for centuries and centuries and this way always produced large crops. When a gardening task is done the same way for a long, long time, we are not anxious to break the habit.

GM: Now we string up the strings the beans will climb on. Here, Declan, take a string and attach it to the u-shaped prong and pull it up like this.

Each one takes a string and tries to attach it to the top of the fence.

Declan: It's way up there above me. Give me some help, please. GM helps for each one.

GF: Now we plant the potatoes. We have two kinds: "Yukon Gold" which is a big one with yellow flesh, and Irish Cobbler, which is a little white potato that is very early and is probably from your Irish heritage. *(The children's mother is from Ireland).*

Liam: Did our Irish grandparents plant Irish Cobbler?

GF: No way of knowing, but they probably did. I have cut up each of the Yukon Gold's into three pieces and we have shaken them up in a paper bag where we have about half cup of sulfur. This is to prevent to prevent rotting in case we have a wet spring. Everyone, take a handful of the yellow Yukon Gold pieces and plant them about a foot apart in this trench I'm making. We don't cover them just yet. Now take handfuls of the Irish Cobblers and plant them about six inches apart. They don't grow as tall as the Yukon's. We also don't cut them apart like we do the Yukon's.

GF: Now we cover them all and pat them down to make sure there are no air pockets near the potatoes. As soon as the first leaves sprout, we will "hill them up, which means to pile more soil on top of where each is planted.

Next is a hill of sweet potatoes. I've been growing cut up pieces of a sweet potato in a box on top of a heat register in the kitchen. See the little leaves that have sprouted from the cuttings? The sweet potatoes are quickly tucked in just so the little leaves are showing. Our next chore is to make newspaper paths between our vegetable rows.

GM: I have a pile of newspapers here. Everybody take four sheets. Now fold all of them in two. Then lay down the folded papers in between each row that is planted. —the row where you have been walking. Keep on until you have finished all the rows. I am going to sprinkle the papers just a little with water from the hose to keep them from blowing away.

GF: I'm next and I have a big bag full of shredded leaves from last fall. We will spread a handful of leaves on top of the papers along the rows until all are covered.

Declan: I can see already that we won't get muddy feet when we work in the garden. Yay!

GM: Before we finish for the day let's all go over to the carrot rows. See the radishes growing in among the carrot foliage? Every one, pull gently on the foliage of one of the radishes. You have now harvested your first vegetable!

GM: We must not forget to plant two rows of the herbs, cilantro and basil. Just make one row on each side of the drip line.

Liam uses the hoe to make the planting rows while GM sows the seeds liberally, covering as she finishes sowing.

GM: Now, Liam, if you will make one more row on each side of the next drip hose, and I will plant marigold seeds in each of those rows.

Liam: We didn't buy marigold seeds, GM. What are they for?

GM: That's right. I saved the seeds from last year's flowers as I do every year. The marigolds are for the bees that will visit them and go on to also visit the pea and bean flowers, and then we will have more peas and beans, and the marigold also look so pretty flowering among the vegetables.

Liam: I like the way you and GF think ahead to what will happen in your garden. I hope I can learn to do that.

Chapter 10
Tomatoes & Peppers

GF: It's May 25th and a fine sunny day and time to plant the tomatoes. Gloves, sunglasses, and bug spray everyone! I will plant the first one and each of you will plant one.

We wait this late in the growing season to plant tomatoes because this is Colorado, and our altitude is 5,280 feet above sea level. Our growing season is short and it's cold at night and takes a long time to warm up in the daytime. When the night temperature goes below 50°F, a tomato does no more growing or ripening.

GF: A tomato plant also has the ability to form roots on its stems. This is something that only a few other plants can do. So we're going to strip off the lower leaves from this plant. Now each of you, use your hands to scoop out the soil to form a long shallow trench, like this. GF makes one of the trenches. Kids follow.

GF plants a tomato, laying it down so that the stem is in contact with the soil; foliage bunches up at end of the trench.

Liam: Aren't the leaves going to grow all sideways?

GF: No, they will perform a trick of facing up to the sun in just a few hours.

Liam: You mean the leaves can move?

GF: They sure can and we will see that they move by five o'clock this afternoon. Now, we all pull the soil over the top of the stems we have buried like this.

GF finishes the planting of the demonstration plant.

Declan: Won't we water these plants?

GF: Yes, but very gently so we don't wash the soil away from where we buried the stems.

Now we place one of these old auto tires that I collected long ago around each plant. The black tires will heat up in the sunlight and let go of the heat during the night. The tires also block the cold winds that come to this area every spring.

Declan: These tires are HEAVY. They aren't going to blow away either!

GF: Very true, Declan, but the neighbors will be stopping by to offer to lend us tomato cages. They think the tires are ugly. Okay, since you're now so good at planting, let's plant the pepper plants GM bought for us. We will put them between the tomatoes. She will put the stakes down where the plants will go. You guys can dig the holes.

GF: Great job. You're getting to be real gardeners! Now we're going to place one of these little stakes next to the stems of each tomato and each pepper plant. These are to prevent cutworms from chewing through each stem.

Melinda: You mean there's a worm that has teeth that can chew this stem?

GF: They don't have teeth, but they do it at night and are very hard to catch them doing it, but if they try, they run into these sticks that they can't penetrate and will move on. We're finished with the peppers and tomatoes, now off you go. Come back this afternoon and you will see that the leaves have turned up to face the sun.

Chapter 11

Sadness

Melinda: Oh, look, GM, here is a big butterfly that fell down!

GM comes immediately to look at the fallen butterfly.

GM: That's not a butterfly, darling, it's a moth. See the little knobs on the tips of its antennae? Butterflies don't have the knobs on their antennae.

Melinda: Why doesn't it fly away? It's alive. See it quivering!

GM: Yes, it's alive, but it may be sick. I have a little cage we could put it in so that it would be safe while it gets well before it can fly away.

She returns with the cage.

GM: Now let's put this little bowl over her, and if she doesn't panic, I will lift it gradually and try to pick her up.

GM successfully picks up the moth and deposits it in the cage.

Ultronia Underwing Moth

Melinda: See how pretty she is. That is such a soft shade of rose on her wings. There isn't any color on her other wings.

GM: Yes, each butterfly and moth has two sets of wings, front and back. They are often different colors.

The moth continues to quiver. GM and Melinda bring a jar lid full of water, but the moth does not drink.

GM: Time to go to bed, little girl.

The next morning Melinda rushes from her bedroom to check on the moth.

Melinda: GM, GM, she is not moving. She's dead, she's dead! (torrents and torrents of tears). The boys come to see the commotion, and also tear up.

GM: Melinda, boys, the moth died, not because she was injured, but because her task in life is over. She has laid her eggs and she has come here to die. She knows that her eggs will hatch into little worms and go on with their life before they pupate, which is when the worm spins a cover, called a cocoon, and after a time inside the cocoon, it will open up and the beautiful moth that looks just like the mother here will emerge. Its wings will dry and unfold and it will begin to fly to search for pollen to eat and water to drink. Her life and death has a name in the scientific world. It is Metamorphosis.

Melinda: But what can we do with her body? We can't just throw it in the trash.

GM: No, indeed, but we can give her a funeral. She hurries to the bedroom and chooses a small box in her dresser drawer, dumps out the jeweled contents and returns with it to the children.

GM: Here is a nice little box that will just fit. It has cotton on the bottom. See the sparkles on the top? Can you lift her and put her in the box? Use your thumb and forefinger to pick her up.

Melinda gently places the moth in the box and closes the lid. "Should we say a verse or sing a song?"

GM: That would be a very nice thing to do. Would you like to start off with saying something nice about her?

Melinda: I would like to tell her how glad I am that she 'choosed' our walk to come to die.

Liam: I'm glad we got to see how a moth lives and dies.

Declan: I'll lead us to sing, "Jesus loves me, this I know, for the Bible tells me so."

All join in to sing this old familiar hymn.[1]

GF: I have made a little place for the box to go. (He has inadvertently dug a fitting hole at the edge of GM's flower garden.)

They all gathered around as GF places the little box in the hole and covers it with soil.

GF: Now we need a tombstone. We can all go to look at my rock collection and choose a tombstone.

They troop off to choose the tombstone.

When one is chosen and placed at the top of the little grave, Melinda announces, "I found you, booteeful moth, and now you are sleeping and we wish you a good time sleeping".

[1] *Footnote: For those of a different faith, please remove this page and insert the blank page to be found at the end of this book.*

That night Melinda has trouble falling asleep and begins to quietly cry, mourning the death of the beautiful moth. GM hears her and enters her bedroom.

GM: I know how sad you are, my darling. Will you let me hold you on my lap in my chair? Melinda mumbles ascent and climbs into her grandmother's lap, legs hanging over the side. Her grandmother begins to gently rock.

Melinda: Nobody never rocked me 'afore.

GM: I'm sure your mother did when you were a baby.

Melinda: Wish I 'membered her.

GM: You do remember her when you are in the quiet places of your mind. Close your eyes now.

Melinda gradually falls asleep and GM lifts her with all the strength she can muster and puts her into her bed.

Chapter 12
Raspberries, Strawberries, Potatoes

GF: Our jobs for today are very easy. We need to fertilize the strawberries and raspberries and pick the ripe ones and hill up the potatoes and pull the leaves from between the Brussel's sprouts, hill up and pull down the news bags on the celery. Boys, hold this fertilizer jar over this bowl and shake out enough to fill it about half full. Walk along the raspberry rows scattering the fertilizer the as you go.

Liam: These little pellets actually have something inside?

GF: Yes and the fertilizer inside will be taken down into the soil along with the water that goes through the drip tubes you see under the row.
Melinda, you take another little bowl and go down each raspberry row to pick all the berries that are real bright red, not shiny. There will be enough to top a bowl of ice cream for each of us for dessert after dinner.

Melinda gathers the berries quickly.

GF: While the boys are finished fertilizing, you and I can tie the raspberry canes to the wires.

Melinda manages to tie a cane to the wire. Like this, GM?

GM: That's very good. We tie them to the wires because they are easier to reach when we pick them, but also because the research by the folks up at the agriculture college tell us that raspberry canes tied to wire produce more berries than if they sprawled on the ground.

Boys: We're done, GF.

GF: Now let's go over to the potatoes to "hill them up", which means we pull more soil from around them and up the stem so that it will branch out and begin to form potatoes.

All three make quick work of hilling up the potatoes.

GF: Now let's do the same hilling up for the celery plants. Then we will slip a newspaper cover over the top of each plant after we have slit the bottom. This operation takes a little longer, but finally each celery plant is standing straight with its pink plastic cover and it leaves sticking out the top..

GM: Now it's time to take care of the strawberry bed that is my domain!

Declan: Are there any ripe ones yet?

GM: No, but they are just turning a little red as you can see. The plants you see are called "Mother Plants" and they were planted last year. Look down here at each side of each mother plant where a little plant called a "runner" formed last fall. Now we fertilize with the same little pellets and soon the fruits will be ready to pick — in about a month.

The children use handfuls of the pellets to scatter around each mother plant.

Liam: This is really complicated, GM. Have you got this all written down someplace?

GM: Yes, little one, I wrote it all down in a little book.

Chapter 13
Weeds

GF: We're going to take a little hike today up into our favorite place, Yellow Wood Canyon. Everyone will need their boots, sunglasses and their gloves, sunscreen and a jacket and a backpack.

Joyous whoops and hollers! They take turns with the sunscreen, put on the boots and gather the gloves, backpack and jackets.

GF: You don't need the jacket yet, but we never go into the mountains without a jacket because you never know what kind of weather might come up very quickly and you could be in serious trouble. So pack the jacket into the backpack.

GM: And here is a lunch for each of you; so put the lunch in the backpack as well. It has a cold pack along with it. There is also a plastic bag for trash and a little packet of seed that we're going to plant.

GF: Everyone ready? Pile into the van and we'll get started.

As they arrive at the base of the trail leading up the canyon, "When is lunchtime" is the chorus.

GF and GM: We might as well eat our lunch now. There is a picnic table and a nice Pinyon pine for shade.

Later.

GF: Have you finished lunch? Now we need to show you what we will be hunting in the canyon. Long ago the grasses that grew here were good food for the deer and elk, and little animals that lived here, but in the last few years another grass has invaded the grass—a real bad grass called Cheat Grass.

Cheat Grass

Children: You mean like cheat on a test? What does the grass cheat?

GF: This grass cheats because if the animals try to eat it, it does not furnish any food for them. In fact, they will only try to eat it once and then move on to try to find some good grass to eat, but the Cheat Grass has crowded out the good grass and the animals have to search farther and farther and often don't find anything to eat.

Declan: Let's go find some Cheat Grass. Everyone straps on the backpacks and they start off up the canyon.

GF: Here is the first stand of Cheat Grass! Gather around and see how easy it is to pull. See, all I have to do is tug and it comes up in my hand. Everyone, take up a handful and see how easy it is.

GM: Now reach into your backpack and pull out that empty plastic bag. That will hold the Cheat Grass. If we just dropped it down to the ground, all those seeds that you see would germinate and a new stand would grow. Now take out your seed packet.

GF: We're going to plant this seed mix of the native grasses of Colorado, but first we scuff up the ground a little. He uses his gloved hand to scratch up the soil. Now scatter a little of the seed, not all because as we hike up the canyon we will come to many more stands of Cheat Grass to pull and re-seed. Now scatter a little of the seed and pat some of the soil to cover it. Rain is predicted soon so it will be ready to germinate and grow quickly. Let's go on up the trail to see if we find any more Cheat Grass.

The following day.

GF: Today we've had a little rain so it's a good day to go after weeds that must be pulled not in our own yard but in our neighbor's. The good deed we did yesterday will be the same today because if we let the neighbor's weeds grow, the seeds that drop will be where new weeds will grow and the seeds will blow over to our land. The neighbor's are in England this month and I told them I would keep the weeds pulled on their place.

Liam: I see some big tall plants that don't look like any in GM's flower bed. Are those weeds?

GF: They are, for sure. This is Canada thistle and we know it is just right for spraying because the flower buds are coloring to the right shade of purple. We're going to kill it by placing this bottomless cardboard box over it like this. Canada Thistle came into this country from the fields of it in Canada long ago. We're going to spray it with glyphosate. The reason for the box is that the spray would go all over nearby good plants, but if we spray it down inside this box it only goes on the thistle. Everyone take a turn with using the spray.

Canada Thistle

Melinda: I don't see the Canada thistle dying very fast. Should we spray more?

GF: No, you all sprayed a good amount, but it will be a week or more before it begins to wilt and die.

GF: The next weed we will tackle is a tiny little one called Bindweed. It looks small and insignificant, but it is one of the worst enemies a gardener can have. See it here? It is a creeper that doesn't look very vicious, but it can have roots that have been found twenty feet down below. It is very hard to kill, but I have here three pairs of scissors, one for each. The scissors will fit right into the holster that comes with them. Now take your scissors and cut the plant off right level with the soil. That's right, now throw the foliage in your bag and we'll look for another one.

Declan: Won't the plant grow right back?

GF: Yes, it will, but it will have to gather up the strength to do that, and then we will be right back and cut it off again and

Bindweed

again, until November. By then all the other plants in the garden will have been killed by the frost, but the bindweed will still be green. That's when we spray it with glyphosate, also called Roundup, which will kill it for good.

GF: The next weed grows in our lawn. Its name is Black Medic. See this little yellow flower?

The children get down on hands and knees to try to find the flower.

Black Medic

Liam: Is this one?

GF: Yes, you found one; now try to gently lift its stem until you get back to the place where its root goes into the ground.

This proves difficult and GF finds the root for him.

GF: Now we go back to the root with each of the stems. See, there are about five stems radiating out over the top of the grass. When you have gathered up all the stems in your hand, then use your right hand to pull up until the taproot comes out of the ground, slick as a whistle!

The children all pull on the taproot and all shout "Slick as a Whistle!" They are delighted that their grandfather has given them yet another colloquialism to tell their parents.

GF: Today we're going to learn to mulch, but first we need to put the second tires on the tomatoes and pick some asparagus. I'll roll the tires out from the garage, and GM will show Melinda the asparagus to pick.

Boys, you put one of the tires on each of the tomato plants. Now the tires have a different job. Instead of protecting the plants from frost and wind, they become a form of mulch to shade the soil and keep it moist, and at the same time they provide a place for each plant to climb around and form strong stems..

Declan: Looks cool, don't you think, Li?

Liam: Yeah, really cool

GF: Now, back to mulching. We open the compost pile to pull out all the dead grass we put there after you mowed the lawn. It has formed fairly good compost so we pile handfuls of it on top of the papers on the paths between the vegetables in the vegetable garden. Then we pile a little of it along each row of raspberries and strawberries. Mulch keeps the soil cool or warm, whichever it needs, and it prevents weeds from growing.

All participate in placing mulch.

Liam: That stuff makes it look uniform, doesn't it?

GM: Now we're going to load up the wheel barrow to take more of the mulch to my flower beds.

All: What's a wheel barrow?

GM: I keep forgetting that you kids don't know the names of all the gardening tools. A wheel barrow just has one wheel, but has a big bin with handles so that anyone can carry a big barrow or bin full of more stuff than they could carry just with their arms. Let's load it up with the mulch.

Chapter 14

Mulch, Mulch

They take turns wheeling the wheel barrow to the flower beds.

Liam: The flower beds look wet, GM. Should we pile the mulch on the wet dir- I mean soil?

GM: That is the best way. When the soil is moist and we put mulch on top, it keeps the moisture in the soil and prevents the weed seed from germinating.

GF: Remember when we left a row to plant turnips until after the summer solstice? Well, now it's June 22nd. Time to plant that row with turnip seed. Let's see if you can find that row.

All: Here it is, GF, we did not forget!

GF: Good for you. Here is the seed and the Warren hoe.

Liam: I'm opening the double row on either side of the drip hose, GF.

Declan: I've got the hose to wet down the row.

Melinda: I've got the seed and I finally get to plant a seed!

Liam: I'll turn over the hoe and cover the seed.

Melinda: I'll pat it down with my feet very carefully!

GF: And I will sprinkle it lightly and place the marker.
We're a Team! Now we need to cut asparagus. Here is a sharp knife for each of you. Please be careful with it. Choose the big fat stems and cut each stem right at the soil line. Put them in this basket. They will taste fine for dinner.

GM: Let's go and make a list of the things we have done this week so we can tell your parents when we skype .

Chapter 15
Insects (and Spiders)

GM: There are aphids on my roses, Well, shall we show the
children one of the down sides of gardening?

Aphid

GF: It's time, for sure. I hope they aren't squeamish because the
best way to kill aphids is with your fingers.

GM: They will be wearing their gloves anyway. So we will see.

Actual Size

GF: I'll get the magnifying glass and round them up. Hey, everybody, it's time
to see one of the Wonders of the World!

All gather around and GM and GF lead them to the rose garden.

GM: Now let me show you a cluster of aphids. This is a tiny little bug the
sucks the nutrients out of the leaves of plants. Can you see them?

Children: I see them, but they are dead, aren't they?

GM: No, they're far from dead. They just have their sucking mouth parts
attached to the leaf. And they don't move much. Here, use the magnifying glass
to see them.

Liam: They hide under the leaf so people can't see them, right?

GM: That's exactly right, Liam. Other bugs want to eat them as well. It's the
old "Survival of the Fittest". It's also so that rain won't wash them away. Now the
best way to kill them is with your fingers. You just wipe them off of the leaf.

Melinda: Oh, squish! I can do that! The boys follow by selecting nearby leaves to wipe aphids off with their fingers

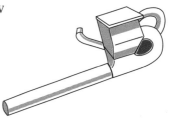

GM: It's easy to see, isn't it, that we are not going to be able to kill them all by standing here and wiping leaves one at a time. So we use a chemical dust to cover them. Their bodies can't breathe under the dust and they die. She demonstrates the duster.

GF: Now you can take turns using the duster.

GF: Now the next insect we're going to study is the Earwig. This is one that goes way back in history. It is small, usually black and has pincher-like legs at the back. It chews holes in leaves and can be a nuisance if it gets into the cabinets in the house, and it has very interesting habits. Let's look at one through the magnifying glass.

All get a chance to look.

Declan: Does it bite people by pinching them with those pincers?

Earwig

GF: We don't think so. It's just that people are afraid that one will get in their nose or in their ears.

GM: Oh, Will, that was a bad picture to put in their heads!

GF: You're right. Kids, that is never going to happen to you. Now here is another interesting thing about the earwig. When it lays its eggs, it lays them near the pod of grasshopper eggs. When the grasshoppers hatch, the baby earwigs eat them. This is sort of another way to control your enemies.

Liam and Declan: Gruesome!

Melinda: I think that's neat!

GF: The last bug we're going to see is the coolest! It's a big bug that is especially fond of eating worms. It's the Preying Mantis. It will eat anything that moves, including its own sisters or brothers. I wish I had one to show you. I haven't seen one in our garden this year, but I know they are here.

Praying Mantis

Melinda: That is so mean! Aren't there any animals that love one another?

GF: Not that I know of in the insect order. But you already know that in the higher order of animals, such as dogs, cats, horses, and many others—they do love and protect each other. Let me show you a picture of the Preying Mantis.

Children gather around.

Liam: Wow, that looks like a miniature dinosaur!

GF: That's a good description. I wish I could show it to you in action. These legs all have joints that let them grasp, take hold of a worm or fly or any other insect. They are slow-moving in comparison to a fly, but once they have hold of their prey they hold it up to their mouth with the two front legs and slowly eat it, just like you and I would eat an ice cream cone. Their eyes can move in the socket and follow you as you move around. They have wings but they seem to hate to fly, and only fly away at the last minute as you approach them or if they are threatened by something such as a flyswatter.

Declan: I've just got to see this bug alive. Do they have one at the zoo?

GF: Beats me, but they might have one at the Butterfly Pavilion, which we should visit sometime soon.

All agree that they hope to see a Preying Mantis soon.

GF: Now I want to bring up the subject of spiders. Is there anyone here who is afraid of spiders?

There is an uncomfortable silence. No one wants to admit they are afraid of spiders.

Spider

GF: Well, that's good to know. I hope I never, never see you destroy a spider. They are the good guys. Spiders will not harm you unless you are threatening them, and then the bite is not fatal, though it can be painful. There are only two spiders in this state that may bite you—the Black Widow and the Brown Recluse. The widow is named because she eats her mate; the recluse is named for the hiding places where it prefers to live. The widow is black with a red spot on her tummy. The recluse is brown. You will probably never see one. All spiders eat insects. They do not eat plants or anything dead. So if a spider gets into our house, we just pick it up in a tissue and take it outdoors and place it on a leaf or near a living insect so that you can watch it pounce on its prey.

Chapter 16

Disease

GF: We don't have many plant diseases in Colorado, and we think it's because our atmosphere is so dry and because our native plants are adjusted to the climate. Also, they are not crowded, so if a disease appears, it does not spread to the next plant easily. But I'm going to show you three diseases we might see during this growing season.

GF: Here is one called POWDERY MILDEW. See this white powdery surface on this lilac leaf? This disease causes the leaf to curl and quit doing its job as a leaf. We don't have many ways to fight it. I just pull off the affected leaves like this and I keep a plastic bag in my pocket to put trash. Next March at pruning time, I will prune out the branches that touch on this lilac as well as the others in the yard.

GF: The next disease we want to look at is FIRE BLIGHT. This is our beloved apple tree. However, I noticed one small symptom of a problem when I saw that limb up above that has one twig that is dark colored, as though it had been burned. If we left that twig on the branch, the disease would travel inside the twig down into the branch; then if I didn't take off that branch, it would travel on down the trunk and kill the tree. So we're going to take off that twig and put it in the trash bag. Your eyes are better than mine. Look at the tree and tell me if you see any more dark-colored twigs.

Children examine tree closely.

Melinda: We don't see any, GF.

GF: Good, now the next disease is not in our yard, but in our neighbor's lawn. Let's walk over to their lawn.

Now we see this lawn kind of looks like it has an insect problem, but it's a disease called NECROTIC RING SPOT.

Children: Is it catching? Can we get it?

GF: No, in no way, it just makes the whole lawn look terrible. What we're going to do is rake all this dead grass up from these spots and put it in our trash bags; then we're going to spread this wheelbarrow of sand over all the spots.

This endeavor takes a half hour or more.

Liam: Wow, the sand makes the whole lawn look much better.

GF: Now the grass plant roots that are still under the sand will be ready to grow normally and up through the sand.

Declan: Will it look good by next year?

GF: Probably, but time and weather will tell. If there are no heavy rains as the grass plants begin to grow, it will have an easier time of recovering.

Chapter 17
The Big Hike

GF: Liam, when you first got off the plane here in Denver you asked where are the Rocky Mountains. We took a small hike into the foothills to show you how to get rid of Cheat Grass, but now we want to take a big hike up into the mountains so that you will see how really grand they are. Tonight get a good night's sleep and we'll leave fairly early tomorrow morning.

The children are excited but obedient in going to bed early and are ready to go much earlier than the grandparents the next morning.

GF: Okay, kiddos, while GM packs the car I'll give you the rules of hiking. The trail we're going to take is called The Devil's Backbone.

Children: Yay, sounds like there will be lots of rocks to climb over.

GM: Not exactly, but we will be climbing right next to this rock formation that looks like it could be the backbone of some giant animal. The trail is also one where hikers are allowed to bring their dogs. We know you like dogs, but when you meet a hiker who has a dog, you are the one to step aside off the trail so that they can pass.

Melinda: Can we pet the dog?

GM: Absolutely not. We never know when it is a friendly dog that likes to be petted, but it's best not to find out. The next rule is to step aside when we meet a person on a horse or if a horseback rider is coming up behind us, we step aside off the trail to let them pass. The next is bicycles. It's best to let them pass as well.

The last rule is the most important of all. It is LEAVE NO TRACE. We never, never leave even a tissue, a wad of chewing gum, a sandwich wrapper — NOTHING! When we pass, we try not to disturb the rocks we climb over as well.

They travel in the car to just outside the Front Range city of Loveland. Everyone unloads and straps on the backpacks, puts on their gloves, and sprays each other with bug spray.

As they walk slowly up the trail GF draws their attention to the backbone-like rocks. They take pictures and are encouraged to move along because the trail is long.

GM who is the birder of the family points out to the children the variety of birds that are in the air.

GM: We want to keep our eyes peeled for the birds of prey. The Peregrine Falcon will be seen practicing their diving stunts.

Declan: Do birds really dive in the air?

GM: They do and they can reach speeds of fifty miles per hour when they are diving on a duck, for example. If the duck is flying below them, they fly straight down at it, hitting and killing it instantly, I have seen this twice in my lifetime and count myself lucky.

Children: Wow! I see a big black bird up ahead, is that a Peregrine Falcon.

GM: No, but it is a very interesting bird. It is a raven. It mates for life and you will see where they nest in the Keyhole up ahead. It's a hole in the rock that is shaped like a keyhole. The birds thought it was a fine hiding place for their nest.

The party stops to rest and to examine the abandoned nest.

GM: Now it's time to take a big drink. Hiking takes a lot of energy and makes you very thirsty for water.

Everyone drinks heartily and they move on. At this point the trail moves westward into higher and higher areas,

GF: We're coming to an area where rattlesnakes have been seen.

Gasps and Shudders!

GF: Don't be afraid. They are much more afraid of you and you are of them. Just be watchful of everything around you, including the sides of the trail where there are bushes and where they may be. They will strike at you if they are threatened. Just don't step on one.

All agree that is the last thing they will ever do.

As the trail heads upward, heavy breathing is heard and GF slows down.

GF: The reason we are all breathing so fast is that the altitude has risen. We are now at about seven thousand feet above sea level and the air has less oxygen. They marvel that less oxygen makes them breathe faster, but at last they reach the top of the trail.
This is the most spectacular view that I can show you today. They all admire the view below of the Great Plains.

GF: The Plains are eight hundred miles wide. These are the Plains that the first settlers in their covered wagons had to cross.

Liam: It must have been very, very hard. We've seen movies of it. But it's more impressive when you really see it.

GM: Lunch is next.

The children are more than ready and quickly pick out sitting rocks.

After they pack up the lunch trash, they move just a little way up to the top where the big snow-covered peaks rise high in the sky.

GF: Liam, this view is a small part of the Rocky Mountains that you were so anxious to see.

Liam: Will I ever get to climb one of those peaks? Is that snow on top? How high are the ones that are white on top?

GF: There are 64 peaks in Colorado that are over 14,000 feet high, and there are so many peaks that are 13,000 feet high that we don't name them.

GF: Of course. When you get a little older you will want to join a climbing club where the first thing you will learn is that no one ever, ever climbs alone. We hear of so many tragic accidents made by climbers who made one slip and no one found them until it was too late.

Liam: I could see on this trail today that there are many places for a slip or a slide and it's a long way down.

GM: Now let's talk of more pleasant things. Look here at the wildflowers near the trail. This is Indian Paintbrush. See how it's bright orange is a signal? The Indians used it, mixed with other plants, in the paint for their faces. Here is Hedge Mustard, which the Indians and probably the settlers used as a flavoring just like we put mustard on our burgers. But over up on that ridge where that little stream

61

comes down is a stand of Water Hemlock, which is a deadly poison. We never put anything in our mouths until we can identify it, and, children, you have many more years of learning about living in the Mountain West.

Now that she has pointed out the little stream, she goes on to tell them it is the beginning of the Big Thompson River. I know it looks small and cute right now, but in 1976 we had a huge amount of rain in one night and this river rose up to half a mile wide and thirty feet deep. It killed over one hundred people. Then in 2013 we had another big rain, but this one was in the daytime and people had time to get out, but the water took out many homes that were along the riverbank.

Later that night.

GF: I hope we instilled in them today a sense of this place, this Mountain West.

GM: I think we did. It was good for them to see the vastness of this state. They have lived in so many confined spaces in their young lives.

Chapter 18

First Harvest

GM: Let's put on sunscreen, sunglasses, bug spray, and gloves, and go out to pick some lettuce and pull some radishes.

Everyone troops outside to the vegetable garden.

GM: I brought a basket and some shears for each. Now I want you to cut the lettuce plants above the ground about this high.

They look at the plant she is cutting to see how high to cut, and begin cutting each plant and placing it in their basket.

GM: We will be able to cut the lettuce again in about three weeks because it will grow again from these stubs that we are leaving.

Now we go over to the carrot row and you can see a different color of foliage from the delicate carrot stems. These are the radishes you will remember planting in the carrot row. You sampled the radishes a few weeks ago. Now we'll harvest more of them. Put your fingers down nearly to the ground to take hold of the foliage. Let's pull them from this row. We'll have radishes on our dinner table for a week or two.

They pull radishes and place them in their basket.

GM: Now we need to plant the seeds of that Halloween pumpkin you are so keen on and the cantaloupe. We don't plant the seeds in cold soil, so the soil is about right now. I have dug a fairly deep hole in my flower garden, and I have filled it almost full of rabbit manure.

All: E-e-oo:

GM: It's all right. It's very old so it does not smell. Now there is about four inches of soil on top of the manure; so here are three seeds, one for each of you. Come and plant them in the soil, and cover the seeds with the soil. Then we will water them in.

As they cover the seeds, GF brings the watering can full of water and they "water in" the seeds, learning a new term as well.

GM: I'm going indoors to wash the lettuce. You all can get out the skate boards or whatever you want to do.

Melinda chooses to follow her grandmother indoors to watch the washing of the lettuce.

GM: We first get the lettuce and radishes into cold water. She fills the sink with cold water and pushes the lettuces and radishes into the water.
See how the specks of dirt fall off an sink to the bottom? We give it one more rinse and then spin the lettuce in the spinner and cut the tops off the radishes.

Melinda marvels at the speed of the spinner that spins the lettuce almost dry.

Later that day as Grandmother begins to fix dinner.

She chops up four slices of bacon and places them in a large skillet.

Melinda: What is the name of what you are making?

GM: It's called Wilted Lettuce, and the recipe was handed down to me by my mother and I'm sure it was handed to her by her mother.

Melinda: So the word "recipe" means directions?

GM: Yes, sorry I forgot that you would not know that word.

Next she fries the bacon until it is crisp; then she pours most of the grease off into a container, and breaks two eggs into the skillet and stirs them until they begin to "set". Then she adds a tablespoon of vinegar before she piles all of the lettuce on top of the bacon and places the glass lid on top.

GM: Now we turn the heat down low and wait for the lettuce to begin to wilt while I finish our dinner.

Melinda is watching all the process of finishing the dinner as Grandmother places the dishes on the table.

All are seated and as Melinda takes a helping of the wilted lettuce onto her plate, she looks down and states, "It looks like throw-up!"

The boys look down at their plate of lettuce, and in tandem with Melinda, jump up and run for the bathroom. All can be heard gagging and vomiting.

GF: Well, that all went south in a hurry, didn't it?

GM: I think it is a demonstration of the Power of Suggestion.

They finish their meal and move to the Family Room to watch the evening news. One by one the children reappear sheepishly and sit down.

GM: You can fix peanut butter and jelly sandwiches if you wish, or your plates, without the lettuce, are in the frig.

They trundle off to the kitchen. The incident is never mentioned again. Next morning the grandparents examine the garden and see that several more crops are ready for the first harvest.

GF: As soon as your lessons are over, you will need bug spray, sunglasses, gloves and your baskets. We're going to harvest some more vegetables.

GF: There are green beans that are small but tender; so we will pick the largest which should be enough for our dinner tonight. Then we will pick a few pea pods and steal a few new potatoes from under the plants. We'll leave the rest to get big for Thanksgiving dinner.

Next is spinach. It's big enough to make a nice salad.

GM: We'll use Shirley Ela's recipe.

Later GM is in the kitchen. Melinda is standing on a little stool to watch the making of the spinach salad.

Melinda: Who is Shirley Ela?

GM: She is a good friend of mine and a very good cook. When we ladies exchange recipes we always keep the giver's name on the recipe card so that many generations from now other cooks will know and remember her name. The green beans are ready to be snapped. Would you like to learn how to snap a bean?

Shirley Ela's Spinach Salad

We pull apart about six cups of washed spinach and place in a large bowl
Then we add one cup of chopped pecans, and one and a half cups of dry-curd cottage cheese.
Next we put the dressing in a small bowl:
1 cup sour cream
¼ cup of sugar
3 tablespoons of wine vinegar
1½ teaspoons of dry mustard
4 tablespoons of horseradish
1 and 1/2 teaspoons of salt
Mix thoroughly and dress the greens. Serve at once.

Melinda: Does that mean I'm going to smash it?

GM: No, you just snap off the tip that held the bean to the stem, like this.

Melinda soon has all the beans snapped and ready for the pot. Next the potatoes are scrubbed and the peas are popped, radishes topped and the makings of a cream sauce for the potatoes are collected.

As the dinner is completed the boys and GM gets washed up and ready to be seated. When Grandfather has seated Grandmother, all are seated.

Chapter 19
Fourth of July

GF: Today is one of the most important holidays in America—the celebration of the date the Declaration of Independence was signed.

Boys: Do we read it?

GF: We do, indeed, and we have ordered copies of it for each of you. But first we must put up the flags.

The flags are removed from the closet.

GF: We unfurl each one and the American flag goes in this socket on the porch pillar. Liam places the flag.

GF: And the Colorado flag goes on the other porch pillar. How do they look?

They all agree they look great.

Liam: The Colorado colors of the flag have meaning, don't they GF?

GF: Yes, the blue is for the blue sky; the white is for the snow; and you both can tell me what the gold stands for, can't you?

Declan: I'll bet it has something to do with the gold that was mined.

GF: You are right. It also stands for all the minerals that have been mined from the mountains. You know, the mining engineers tell us that ninety two percent of the gold is still inside those mountains. That's why we see mines still being worked, but it's a hard, hard job.

In the afternoon Grandmother baked the birthday cake. It is always an angel food cake with brown sugar frosting. The children play with the neighborhood children on the slope or with the soccer ball.

In the early evening the entire neighborhood gathers for a POT-LUCK. This is a new word for the children. It is explained that the word evolved many years ago from each neighbor bringing the pot of what they could share to a table, and it was the luck of everyone that it all turned out to be a celebration. Grandmother's offering to the food table is the angel food cake.

Children, GF and GM: Look at all these foods! All are labeled. There are baked beans, cucumbers and sour cream, orange slices and sugar, pickled beets, carrot sticks, corn and tamale casserole, red cabbage with apples — and cherry pie, fudge brownies, and your cake, GM.

GM: After you fill your plates, go over to the barbecue and pick out a wiener or a bratwurst. Put it in a bun and pile on all the toppings you want.

The children experience their first POT LUCK, and are anxious to tell their parents about it when they skype the following day.

After dinner everyone quiets as Grandfather reads the Declaration of Independence. Tears come to the old folks eyes as the final words are read: "And for the support of this Declaration, with the firm reliance on the protection of Divine Providence, we mutually pledge to each other our lives, our fortunes, and our sacred Honour".

Declaration of Independence

When, in the course of human events, it becomes necessary for one people to dissolve the political bands which have connected them with another, and to assume, among the powers of the earth, the separate and equal station to which the laws of nature and nature's God entitle them, a descent respect to the opinions of mankind requires that they should declare the causes which impel them to the separation.

We hold these truths too be self evident, that all men are created equal; that they are endowed by their Creator, certain unalienable rights; that among these are life, liberty, and the pursuit of happiness; that, to secure these rights, governments are instituted among men, deriving their just powers from the consent of the governed; that whenever any form of government becomes destructive of these ends, it is the right of the people to alter or abolish it, and to institute new government, laying its foundation on such principles, and organizing its powers in such form, as to them shall seem most likely to effect their safety and happiness Prudence, indeed, will dictate; that governments long established should not be changed for light and transient causes; and, accordingly, all experience hath shewn, that mankind are more disposed to suffer, while evils are sufferable, than to right themselves, by abolishing the forms to which they are accustomed. But when a long train of abuses and usurpations, pursuing invariably the same object, evinces a design to reduce them under absolute despotism, it is their right, it is their duty to throw off such government, and to provide new guards for their future security. Such as been the patient sufferance of these colonies, and such is now the necessity which constrains them to alter their former systems of government. The history of the present king of Great Britain is a history of repeated injuries and usurpations, all having in direct object the establishment of an absolute tyranny over these states. To prove this, let facts be submitted to a candid world.

We, therefore, the representatives of the UNITED STATES OF AMERICA, in General Congress assembled, appealing to the Supreme Judge of the world for the rectitude of our intentions, so, in the name and by the authority of the good people of these colonies, solemnly publish and declare, that these United Colonies are, and of right ought to be, FREE AND INDEPENDENT STATES; that they are absolved from all allegiance to the British crown and that all political connection between them and the state of Great Britain, is, and ought to be, totally dissolved, and that, as FREE AND INDEPENDENT STATES may of right to do. And for the support of this declaration, with a firm reliance on the protection of Divine Providence, we mutually pledge to each other our lives, our fortunes, and our sacred honour.[1]

In Congress July 4, 1776

[1]Footnote: The Declaration was signed in Philadelphia. Riders were dispatched carrying copies of it to the newspapers (Gazettes) of each capital city of each state. The above was copied from the Virginia Gazette in Williamsburg, Virginia.

The families all retreat to their own homes to watch the National Concert. In truth, the entire nation comes together every year on this date to watch the National Concert on television where thousands of people gather on the lawn of the Capital Building in Washington for the Marine Band and the Symphony Orchestra to entertain. The music is varied: classical with well- known opera stars singing; "country" with famous country music stars, finishing with martial music from the Marine Band. Many of the people enjoy dancing or marching on the lawn and singing the old familiar songs.

The concert ends with the playing of "The 1812 Overture" when live canons are shot off at the intervals in the music that represent a battle at sea during the war of 1812. As the canon fire ends, the beginning of a truly spectacular fire works display begins. Fireworks have been forbidden in Littleton for many years, so the children and grown-ups are exclaiming with oh's and ah's as each explosion is greater than the last.

GF: Well, what did you think of our celebration of the Fourth of July".

Liam: I have written it all down, GF, because wherever we are every Fourth the July, we will try to celebrate in this same way every year.

GM, you have to be there to bake the cake!

Everyone laughs and they go off to bed.

Chapter 20
Tomatoes, Tomatoes

GF: I know we've all been watching the tomatoes. They have been red for about a week now, which means that they are probably at their peak of ripeness and it's time to pick.

Shouts of joy and there is a rush to get the picking baskets.

GM: Now I want to show you how to twist the fruit and gradually it will release from the stem. Watch me.

GM holds each fruit in her hand and gradually twists the fruit until it falls into her hand. There are about a dozen that are ripe enough to pick, so all of you try your hand at picking.

GF: I see that the little San Marzano tomatoes are now ready also. Shall we pick some, Grandmother?

GM: We'll pick just four of them to make some Salsa, and leave the rest for a few days to get really ripe.

GF: Now that we've picked our first tomatoes, what are we going to do with them?

SHOUTS OF JOY "BLT'S, BLT'S, BLT'S".

They rush indoors. Liam gets the bacon out of the frig and begins to separate the slices onto a paper plate.

Declan get's the special tomato-slicing knife out and places it beside five tomatoes to be waiting for Grandmother to slice them. Lettuce leaves are chosen and washed.

Melinda begins smearing mayo on ten slices of bread. Grandmother places the plate of bacon in the microwave and sets it at 2 minutes. When the time is up, GM removes the paper plates of bacon and drains off the grease into a container. She has sliced the tomatoes and now the assembly begins. Tomatoes first, then bacon, then lettuce, then topped by second slice of bread. Lunch is served and all thoroughly enjoy BLT's.

Later in the afternoon, GM asks, "Melinda, would you like to watch another recipe?"

Melinda: Sure, whatever it is you're making, I'm interested.

GM: I'm going to make Salsa for our corn chips that we bought in the market today. First I need to get out the recipe. She leafs through the cards in her recipe box. I'm looking for Lucy Pettison's Salsa. It's the best we have ever had. Sure enough. Here it is and it has her name on it. Remember how I told you that we are always very careful to keep the name of the person who gave you the recipe?

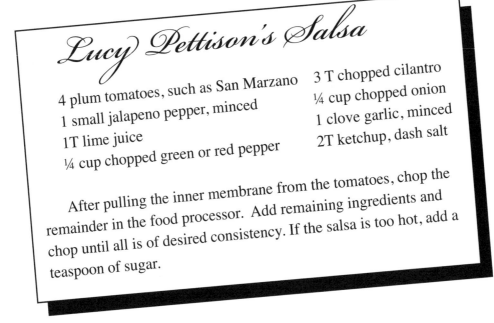

Lucy Pettison's Salsa

4 plum tomatoes, such as San Marzano
1 small jalapeno pepper, minced
1T lime juice
¼ cup chopped green or red pepper

3 T chopped cilantro
¼ cup chopped onion
1 clove garlic, minced
2T ketchup, dash salt

After pulling the inner membrane from the tomatoes, chop the remainder in the food processor. Add remaining ingredients and chop until all is of desired consistency. If the salsa is too hot, add a teaspoon of sugar.

GM: See how easy it is with every ingredient going into the food processor?

Melinda: I'm not good with using a knife, so the food processor is for me.

GF: Yes, here's the chips, try it, Melinda.

Melinda: Oh, wow, that is really hot. My eyes are watering, but I love it!

Chapter 21

The Corn Trip

GF: Today we have just two or three chores before we get into the van and drive to Olathe. Remember when I told you that we don't have room to grow corn, so we let the folks in Olathe do it for us? This is the season when the corn is at its best, so we'll buy what we want to freeze and to eat fresh. But first, gloves, hats, and bug spray; and then we'll get to it

GM: I have a bucket of fertilizer: 10-10-10 are the numbers for nitrogen, phosphorous, and potassium.

GM instructs them how to take a TABLESPOON scoop of fertilizer and gently spread it at the side of the rows of beans, potatoes, sweet potatoes, and lettuce. Then she hands out "scratchers" to scratch the fertilizer in. The children carefully fertilize each plant.

GM: We must not forget your watermelon and your pumpkin. They have been growing well with the drip irrigation, but now it's time to give them an extra push to put on some weight. The children water and fertilize the watermelon and the pumpkin.

GF: After the van is packed with cartons and lunches. GF announces the last bathroom stop.

As they return from the bathroom, GM loads extra jackets and a blanket. She warns: "We're going into the high country today, children. Remember, that means we never leave home without packing extra jackets and a blanket. They could save our lives if we should have an accident and be left stranded until someone finds us."

The children are sober with thoughts of an accident as they climb into the van.

The traffic is heavy on the way up into the mountains, but it is a 4-lane highway and it is easy to get to the top of Vail Pass. This is where they make a turn, onto a bridge, over the highway to a rest stop. Everyone piles out to stretch and snack and take pictures of the view.

GM: Back in the van, kids. Now we're going to go over McClure Pass.

Liam: Is the pass named after a person?

GF: Yes, it was named after "Mac" McClure who first discovered it as a pathway used by the Ute Indians who walked over this pass to trade with the Arapahoe tribe on the Plains where we live. Then this pass served as a cattle trail to lead cows down to Denver to be sold. Now it leads to another valley, the North Fork Valley where the North Fork river joins the Gunnison river that takes many turns to join the mighty Colorado. It's a very weather-protected valley where peaches and pears and apples are grown very easily with almost no danger of frost at the bloom time, which is the fear of the fruit growers in the Grand Valley, which is on the other side of the highest peaks. The Grand Valley is where your grandmother and I grew up.

It is a very pleasant drive with Grandfather pointing out the concrete-lined irrigation canal that brings the melt-water down from the snow on the high peaks to the orchards down below.

As they descend to the main highway, they arrive at Olathe. It's easy to see they have arrived because there are miles and miles of corn fields on either side of the road.

Declan: Are we going to pick our own? Will you show us how?

GF: Yes, to both as soon as I am assigned a plot to pick. I'll be back soon.

GM: Let's look closely at the ears of corn. You can see the corn ears growing along the stems. Now look upward to the top of the stems where you see the "tassel". This is full of pollen that drops downward to touch the silky strands that are tip of each the ears. Each strand receives one portion of pollen and "voila" the corn begins to grow each kernel of corn. Now we don't pick every ear of corn in our plot. We pick only those that are ripe, and ripe means "square or blunt" on the end. Here's GF with our plot assignment. So out of the car, please. Bug spray, sunblock, hats, gloves are needed.

GM: Here are the picking sacks that go around your necks. Follow me to our plot.

GF: Watch me pick a stalk now. He demonstrates squeezing the tip of an ear to make sure it is square, and then stripping the ear from the stalk and dropping it into the sack. Easy, huh?

GM: I think we've picked about 100 ears. At least, we have come to the end of our plot and I don't think we have missed a "square" ear.

All agree and they pack the ears into the cartons in the car.

GM: Now with air-conditioning in the car, our corn will remain cool until we are home.

With a stop for a picnic lunch in the Olathe town park, they are soon home and unpacking the corn. GM brings down a very large fry-pan from the pantry shelf. She drops two cubes of butter into it and turns the burner on low.

GF and the children set up large plastic baskets on the lawn and everyone takes a seat on a folding chair.

Watching GF, the children grab ears of corn and begin stripping the wrapper leaves and silk off the ears. Finished ears are placed in another basket.

GF: For an unknown reason, all these wrapper leaves and silks are called "shucks". So we are "shuckin" corn.

Back in the kitchen, the butter is melted and GM is cutting the kernels off each ear with a newly invented device that cuts all the kernels into a pile. Now bare, the ears are discarded.

The corn kernels are piled in the skillet and Melinda is pushing the corn around in the butter very slowly. This goes on for an hour before GM declares it is done. There is no more butter to be seen. It has been absorbed by the corn. GM then fills small zip-lock plastic bags with one-meal portions of the corn and hustles them into the freezer.

This process goes on until the corn-to-butter-to bag process is finished and everyone is exhausted.

GF declares: GM is too tired to fix dinner. We're all going to Wendy's for burgers and fries and chocolate frosties. Hurrahs all around.

After they are full to the brim with non-nutritious fast-food, they are ready for an evening of TV, then showers and bed.

Chapter 22

Harvest Again

GF: Today after your lessons we need to get out into the garden to harvest all we can. Our average first frost is October 10, but we do a lot of covering of plants that we can prevent being frozen. For now, however, we can harvest our turnips, cauliflower, cantaloupe, a few Brussel's sprouts, our ripe tomatoes and peppers, the last of the spinach before we sow more in the same row, a few carrots, though carrots can be left in the ground until after frost. So off we go with the wheel barrow to fill it fast.

All three children carefully harvest like they have been taught; then the harvest looks so beautiful in the wheelbarrow, they take pictures of it and with themselves.

GM: Your watermelon got fairly big, didn't it? I think if we carefully set it on top of a tuna fish can it will get more sun and not be down on the cold ground. We'll put a piece of an old bedspread nearby so if frost is predicted some evening, we can rush out and cover it.

Two weeks later.

GF: Let's look at your watermelon again. It's very nice looking, with just a dry stem that shows it is ready to harvest.

Liam: So we don't cut into the melon to see if it's ripe. We just look at the stem, and if it's dry, the melon is ready?

GF: That's the jist of it. Of course, size and weight can easily be estimated, and if it's big and heavy, it's ready to harvest.

Liam takes note of "jist of it" to add to their list of expressions they want to remember.

They weigh the melon and find that it weighs eight pounds.

Chapter 23

Halloween

GM: I know you have all heard of Halloween. It's time to harvest your pumpkin and get it ready with a candle inside to decorate our front porch. Your pumpkin grew tall and crooked, but that will make it all the easier to make it look scary. GF will get out his little electric saw and make a face on your pumpkin. Have you ever put on costumes and gone to a parade of other kids from house to house, asking for a treat?

Liam: We have a book of pictures of the various holiday celebrations, but no, we've never had costumes or celebrated Halloween.

GM: The idea of it is to put on a costume and a mask so that no one will recognize you; than you go to the door of a neighbor and ask for a treat. The theory is that if the neighbor does not give you a treat, you will play a trick on them, such as rubbing soap on their window screens. However, this never happens that I know of. The neighbor laughs. Admires your costume and gives you candy.

Then the parade of kids moves on to the next house. Soon your bag will be full of candy and you will come back here to spread out all your "treats" on the floor to see who has the best or most. So, what costumes will you want?

Liam: I want to be a Pirate with a sword and a pistol!

Declan: I want to be a fireman with a badge.

Melinda: I want to be a ghost!

GF: It will be easy to fulfill those requests at the costume store. Let's go!

They return from the costume store in high spirits, and experiment with wearing the masks and being able to wear their masks and navigate without falling. Melinda's request to be a ghost is the easiest. A torn sheet from the rag-bag and GM's scissors to make eye-holes and the costume is finished.

On the evening of Halloween they set out with neighbor friends to traipse around. GM, on the other hand, has camera in hand as she hides on the front porch. As each group approaches she takes a flash picture, scaring the kids, but then all laugh and ask for a print of the group. She promises to makes many prints. When all return, she tells them she will add all of the pictures to others she has taken over the years.

The children return from their house-to-house adventure, anxious to spread out their loot. The grandparents watch and allow each child a sample of the sweets, before it's off to bed.

Chapter 24
Thanksgiving

GM: Eat your breakfast, kids. This is the day before Thanksgiving and there is lots of shopping to do. I thought you might want to go along to see what the ingredients are for the dinner tomorrow. We need to get to it. *(Melinda makes note of "get to it.")*

Melinda: I want to see all of the foods we choose, but the most fun for me is the cooking!

They arrive at the supermarket and GM goes first to the meat department.

GM: I ordered a 20-pound turkey several weeks ago. It should be ready today.

She loads it into the cart, and moves to pick up two one pound packages of sausage. That will be used in making the dressing. The children take turns pushing the cart.

Next are the vegetables and fruits that are needed.

From the canned goods shelves she chooses canned pineapple, black cherries and pumpkin, and then two fresh Granny Smith apples from the fresh fruit section.

Next she pushes her cart over to the spice and flavorings shelf and chooses dried thyme, dried sage.

In the dried fruit section she chooses dried apricots and dried cherries. In the dried mixtures shelf she chooses cornbread stuffing mix and the chicken broth to moisten it.

GM has completed her grocery list and they move to the check-out line. While they are waiting she explains to the children that she will use her credit card in the same way they saw it used when they were in the garden center to pay for the Thanksgiving items.

GM: Thank you all for unloading the cart for me. You can all go out to play. The boys run off, but Melinda stays behind to watch the proceedings for cooking and baking.

GM: This is the pie-dough mix I use to roll out a dough the size for this pie pan, Melinda. I'm going to bake a mincemeat pie today. It will hold over till the dinner tomorrow. This is the mincemeat filling, and I have cut up the two apples to place on top of the filling. Then we top it with the top crust and place it in the oven at 375 degrees for an hour of baking. I'm going to roll out another dough now for the pumpkin pie tomorrow, but I won't bake it until tomorrow morning. I want it to be just warm when it is served with whipped cream.

Next GM sets aside six of their home-grown Yukon Gold potatoes next to a pot where they will be cooked tomorrow.

She chooses six of their home-grown sweet potatoes to boil now in order to finish preparing them for tomorrow.

She pours the package of corn bread stuffing mix into a large mixing bowl and follows the directions for adding the sausage and finishing the dish except for the chicken broth.

GM: We'll wait until an hour before the turkey is done before we finish the stuffing mix. It has its own pan that fits next to the turkey roaster in the oven.

When the sweet potatoes are soft, they are ready to be peeled, which Melinda is now pronounced an expert. The dish is completed with the canned crushed pineapple and brown sugar, and, of course, butter is added to the pan.

GM laughs: The Thanksgiving Dinner is never low-calorie. There will be more butter added to the mashed potatoes your Mother makes. She makes the best!

GM: The next thing to prepare is the Jello® salad. She opens two cans of black cherries and pours off the juice into a measuring cup, adding enough water to make two cups. She brings this to a boil and adds it to the powdered black cherry Jello® and stirs until all is dissolved.

GM: Now we put it in the frig until it begins to gel; then we add a handful of chopped pecans and the cherries and stir until the fruit and nuts are distributed. The last thing we do today is to take the wrapper off the turkey and take out the giblets.

Melinda: What on earth is a giblet? It sounds like some kind of tool.

GM: No, it means all of the edible inner organs such as the liver, the gizzard, the neck, and the heart. We just put them all in a pot full of hot water and boil them for about an hour. Then we will chop them to make them ready to be added to the gravy.

Melinda: Where does the gravy go?

GM: On top of the mashed potatoes. I'll bet you have never had mashed potatoes and gravy.

Melinda: I don't think so, but it sounds delicious!

GM: The last dish we do today is Spanish Beans. Are you ready to do your bean-snap thing? Melinda is ready and the last of the home-grown green beans are heaped before her and she sets to work snapping the stem ends.

GM fries up six slices of bacon until crisp and pours off most of the grease. Then she adds the contents of a small can of seasoned tomato sauce and a handful of chopped onions. She turns the stove to "low" and adds the beans and cooks the beans until they are tender. They will be warmed to serving temperature tomorrow.

The cherry Jello® is beginning to gel now and Melinda stirs in the black cherries and a handful of chopped pecans. Then the finished salad is covered and placed back in the frig.

GM: I must not forget to put the cranberry sauce in the frig (as she places it there). Now we get out the baking sheets to be sprayed with Pam® and place beside them the containers of brown-and-serve-rolls. The silver basket will be used to serve them.

GF: Okay, boys, time to come in to help me with the dining room table.

The boys and GF come in to the dining room.

GF: We are going to put the leaves into the table. Let me show you where they are stored.

They move to the closet and GF pulls out the leaves; each caries one dining room table leaf.

Liam: Wow, they are heavy!

GF: They are solid mahogany. Your parents had this table and the chairs made in England when they were stationed there. Pull on the end of the table while I hold it steady. They pull and the table splits apart. Each of the leaves is fitted into the table.

See how much longer it is now? It will now seat fourteen which is the number expected tomorrow. Now we put on the table pads that will protect the top from damage from a hot dish. The tablecloth is next. This cloth came from South Korea. During that war we had a young friend who was a fighter pilot for our Air Force. His base was in Japan. When he was on weekend leave, he loved to shop for items that had been made in South Korea. He brought us this embroidered cloth as well as one similar to his mother.

Now we wait for your grandmother to tell us which china and crystal we will use to set the table.

GM to Melinda: I know I can trust you to carry the china and glasses very carefully. She portions out the stacks of dinner plates, salad plates, and bread and butter plates.

GF directs where each is to go saying, "The dinner plates go a foot and a half apart, like this." He motions each place and all are correctly placed.

Now let's place the salad plates at the head of and to the side of the dinner plate like this.

GM: Now lets place the bread and butter plates directly above the dinner plate. We're ready for the silver! Will Henry, have you opened the safe and can you bring it out?

GF: I have and I will. He carries the silver in its silver-cloth case to the table.

GM: Now let's select the knives and place them with the sharp blade inward to the plate and to the right of the plates. This silver belonged to your great-great-grandmother. She lived in Mississippi.

Next let's place the teaspoons at the right of the knives.

This takes awhile because there are several sizes of spoons to choose from. GM points out the correct size.

Next let's go to the other side of the plate and choose the dinner forks. They are the big ones. On the outside of the dinner fork is the salad fork. We are almost done! Lastly is the tiny butter knife that goes on top of the bread-and butter plate with its blade pointing inward like this. Now we begin the glassware.

GF: The crystal is very delicate. I think we should carry them one in each hand. We begin with the water goblets. (This parade of carriers amuses both grandparents).

Next are the wine glasses that go to the left of the water goblet. The same parade ensues. Each of you children will have a teaspoon of the wine in one of these glasses.

Children: Yay! We will be toasting too!

Last of all is the centerpiece. Grandmother brings in the bouquet of red roses arranged in a silver bowl, and the candelabra to be placed on either side of the flowers.

GM wheels in the little cart that is placed to the left of her place at the table. It will hold the warming tray that will keep hot the sweet potatoes, mashed potatoes, gravy, and Spanish beans.

GF: Now it's time to go to the airport to pick up your parents!

Shouts of joy!! And they rush to load into the van.

The next morning all except GM are settled in front of the TV watching the Thanksgiving Day parade up Fifth Avenue in New York City. Each giant floating balloon of a familiar comic brings shouts of joy. The children have never seen anything like this parade.

GM assembles the pumpkin pie and puts it in the oven to bake. She then stands on the stepladder in the pantry to retrieve the turkey roaster inherited from her mother. Melinda hears the rattle of the pan and appears.

Melinda: I can watch the parade and watch you at the same time!

GM: The pie is finished and I will set it in the pantry to cool. Now it's time to get the bird ready to go to the oven.

She opens a huge clear plastic bag and places it in the roaster so that she can add three tablespoons of flour to the bottom of the bag so that the bird will be on top of the flour and the skin will not stick to the pan. She then asks GF to lift the twenty-pound bird into the plastic bag, and he goes back to his chair to watch the parade.

Anne, the children's mother, is busy peeling potatoes and setting them to cook. Melinda helps with the peeling, anxious to be near her mother.

GM finishes mixing the stuffing with broth and packs it into its special narrow pan (a fish poaching pan) to snug up to the side of the roaster in the oven. Both go to the oven, which is set to 350 degrees.

GM brings to the kitchen the hand-painted fruit plates that will be for the pie. She also brings in more forks for serving the pie She lays the plates and forks out on a counter.

She mixes the thickening for the gravy in a small skillet, ready for the stove when needed.

Then she looks around and thinks to herself, "What have I forgotten". Then she remembers the rolls and opens the packages of "brown-and-serve" rolls and places them on a baking sheet ready to be put into the oven. She cuts the black cherry salad into squares and places a square on a lettuce leaf on the salad plates and places each plate on the table. She opens cans of cranberry sauce and pours them into crystal dishes. Then, since she can't find anything else to do, she joins in watching the parade.

At fifteen minutes till one o'clock both grandparents and parents rise and GM announces. Time to change clothes to get ready for dinner everyone.

A short time later the doorbell rings and guests begin arriving—five friends who would otherwise be alone have been invited plus a young couple who have been longtime friends of the children's parents.

Ann gives the potatoes a big dollop of butter as she finishes mashing and pours them into a fancy dish for serving and places it on the warming tray beside GM's chair.

The bird is removed from the oven and removed from its plastic bag and allowed to "settle", meaning juices will settle out of the bird and into the pan below to become the gravy.

GF: Hey, Everyone! If you want to see the carving of the bird, come on out to the kitchen to watch. Everyone assembles in the kitchen. I use an electric knife and it makes it much easier.

He carves the drumsticks first, meaning the thighs and the legs. This is dark meat and it is placed on the waiting platter. Next is the breast, which is white meat. The knife slices perfect slices that are also placed on the platter; the wings are removed last.

The dressing is scooped into a waiting bowl. The juices in the roaster are measured and mixed with the gravy thickener and simmered until thickened and then poured into the gravy boat. The silver ladle is laid by its side.

The vegetables: Spanish beans, sweet potatoes, and mashed potatoes are dished and carried to the electric plate warmer on the cart next to GM's chair.

The platter of turkey, the rolls, and the dressing are carried to the table and all assemble.

GM announces: Please find your chairs at the placecards.

GF: Please stay standing and raise your glasses for the toast.

"Ladies and gentlemen and children, we gather this day for remembrance and thankfulness for those pilgrims who on this day so many centuries ago came together to share what little they had. They didn't know what lay ahead. They had suffered starvation and freezing cold the previous winter. They had accepted with gratitude the help with planting from those first Americans, the native Indians who lived on the shores of what is now Massachusetts. Let us raise our glasses in salute to those brave people."

After the toast GF seats GM and announces "Please be seated."

The returning parents lead the table conversation during dinner, telling all of their travels the past nine months. After dinner everyone retires to watch the football game or to play a board game at the card table.

GF and Liam stand together looking out the window at the garden. It is in disarray and Liam muses, "It's back to the beginning, isn't it?"

GF: Yes, tomorrow we will rake up the dead plants and spade the soil just like you did when you first came.

Liam: I'm anxious to "get to it."

THE END